BLACK

A Love Story

CLARENCE BIRDSONG III

BLACK

A Love Story

Dedication

This book is dedicated to my 4 best friends, my heartbeats, my children:

Brandon, Clarence IV, Brandi, and Brycen

Don't you ever tell me what you can't do.

Acknowledgments

In a time when everyone likes to take sole credit for their success and proclaim to be self-made, I've come to understand that true success cannot be achieved alone. God is always present. It's because of him that I am who I am. I take no part in saying I am self-made. It's great to be self-motivated, self-sufficient, and independent of others. Your talent alone without a team will only get you so far. You must have people around you that bring out your creativity while lending you theirs in an effort to help you do things outside of your skill set.

To Team Birdsong, editor Trina Somerville and graphic designer Colandus Hill (LTG Customs), thank you for sharing in my vision, being trustworthy, and sometimes being lovingly and brutally honest. My dreams have become a reality with the kind of support you offered through this process. There were times, I know, that I pushed to meet deadlines that were seemingly unattainable and got on your nerves every now and then. I can't thank you enough. You helped bring my vision to life and for that I am forever grateful. Thank you.

This book is a work based on realistic events that the author feels plague the black community. Names, characters, places, and incidents are all a part of the author's imagination. Any direct resemblance to events and people are entirely coincidental.

Table of Contents

Real Love...................

Real Talk...............

- **Various Quotes**

Real Love

You Go Girl

Far too often society paints your picture as bitter,
aggressive, angry, and loud

But forgive them, 'cause you see, they don't truly know
who you are and what you're about.

They don't fully understand the weight you carry.

If they truly had to walk a mile in your shoes

And were able to get a sneak peek of what you really go
through

They'd back off, because it's too scary.

They don't understand the physical and sexual abuse
you may have gone through that didn't break you,

You let it use you as a breakthrough

And you're still standing.

Family and everybody wrote you off because you were a
teenage mother, barely completed high school

Told you, 'You ain't gonna be nothing!'

But you're still standing.

That man left you after four kids and all those invested years

It didn't break you

And you're still standing.

Struggling to raise kids by yourself

Doing what you can to make sure your kids have something to eat, even if it means you starve.

Watching people turn up their noses and judge you once you pull out the WIC and EBT cards.

On the job, they look at your complexion and say, 'It must've been affirmative action.'

But they don't know the HELL you went through just to climb that corporate ladder

The sleepless nights, the thousands of dollars you still owe for those college classes.

Now, I get the bigger picture.

They confuse your passion as aggression,

Your relentless, "no quit" attitude as anger

Your no-nonsense attitude as bitter 'cause not every guy who calls themselves a man can get wit ya'

So BOLD

So Beautiful

So STRONG

When you continuously win Wimbledon after Wimbledon

Gold Medal after Gold Medal

One power corporate position after another seemingly shocking the world.

I laugh to myself a little 'cause, it's nothing new to me.

Black girls BEEN Magic!!

And in my 'Martin' voice, "YOU GO GIRL!!"

You're Beautiful Period!

From the way you walk, your confidence, the way those jeans fit the curves in your hips

The fullness of your figure and the fullness of your lips

You're not just Beautiful for a BIG girl

You're Beautiful PERIOD.

With a smile that lights up the room, and a personality that takes it over

Your sense of style and your grace is so SERIOUS

You're not just Beautiful for a BIG girl

You're Beautiful PERIOD.

Yeah you weigh more than the average chick, but you wear it so well

Yeah, they may be smaller, but your face is sexier

You're not just Beautiful for a BIG girl

You're Beautiful PERIOD.

Melanin popping, skin kissed by the sun with an attitude
to match

Light brown eyes of fire burning so bright, as if someone
struck a match

You're not just Beautiful for a DARK-skinned girl

You're Beautiful PERIOD.

You bleed sensuality

Never seen skin so smooth, so tight

You can be 50 and still look 25 with no wrinkles in sight

You're not just beautiful for a DARK-skinned girl

You're Beautiful PERIOD.

People see you and they're so amazed by your beauty
they don't know how to approach you

As if being your complexion and looking that fine isn't
something you're supposed to do

Just because you're DARK-skinned you're supposed to
go unnoticeable

So, the next time they get brave enough

Thinking they're giving you a compliment

Saying, 'YOU'RE PRETTY FOR A DARK-skinned girl.'

Say, "Are you serious? That's an insult to MY BEAUTY.

I'm not just pretty for a DARK-skinned girl ...I'm
BEAUTIFUL PERIOD!!!"

You're So Much More Than That

Yo' Fellas...

I know that the media and the news like to portray you
as violent criminals and thugs

But you're so much more than that.

They are quick to blast the dropout and incarceration
rates,

But they hide from you Graduation rates

They want you to believe that all you'll ever do is run
fast and jump high,

But you're so much more than that.

They'll highlight your athletic ability

But at the same time, you can't compete with the rest of
the world academically

They say if you can't make it on the court or the field
then you're more likely to run the streets

Sell drugs, end up in jail, and If you're lucky you'll bus tables, work in a warehouse or fast food place

Living paycheck to paycheck

But you're so much more than that.

You weren't created just to be athletes

You too are inventors, lawyers, doctors, entertainers, CEO's and COO's of Fortune 500 Companies,

great fathers, and husbands

An asset to society.

Hey Ladies...

I know all the media portrays you as sex toys, sex objects, and video vixens

But you're so much more than that.

They are quick to give you the numbers on teenage pregnancy, food stamps, and section 8 recipients

But less likely to tell you the success rate of the black woman

They want you to believe that all you'll ever be is a nice backside

All you'll ever be good for is to lay on your backside

But you're so much more than that.

They'll highlight your curves and your beauty

But diminish the power of your brain.

They say if a stripper pole or twerking is not attached

Then you won't be successful

And if you miss out on those talents

You'll most likely end up a manager at a department store

But you're so much more that.

You were not created to be objects of affection

You too are some of the brightest minds the world has ever seen

The most creative beings ever created

The most gracious athletes, entertainers, and business women

All while pulling double duty as the brilliant, inspiring mothers that...

You ARE.

Colors

Dark skin, Light skin

Dark skin, light skin

All skin is the right skin

Only our people act like "light" skin and "dark" skin are
two different races

Not fully understanding that underneath that
complexion we share the same faces

The same struggles

Just because he's darker or lighter than you

How can you hate your brother?

Too powerful together, so they decide to divide and
conquer

Too many slaves escaping, so let's put them against each
other

The lighter you are, the closer to the master's house
you are

The darker you are, the further you are

It worked too.

Oh!

What did that do?

It made you despise someone that looked just like you

The darker skinned hated the lighter skinned, because they got certain privileges

They didn't have to work as hard

They could stay in the house and be cool

Meanwhile the lighter skinned look down on the darker skin

As if they were better, because they were in a better situation than you

But not realizing completely that they were slaves too.

What's even more amazing?

This simple-minded thinking has been passed down from Generation to Generation.

Some are ashamed to even be classified as black, especially if they're biracial

Leaning more toward their *other* side of the *family*

And if they're just black and have a good grade of hair

They blame it on the Indian in their family

They told you

They showed you

They gave you what beautiful was

And made You hate You

Meanwhile, they're creating more plastic surgeries, so they can look more like yooooou!!!

You can't see that truth

But we're walking around talking about I don't date light-skinned dudes

Or I don't date dark-skinned women

Still?

You can't be for real.

Stop allowing divide

To conquer

To continue

To work

And let them win

It......... Doesn't....... **Matter.....**

What your complexion is

Light skin

Dark skin

All skin is the Right Skin ....

BLACK

How Do You Feel About You?

We spend way too much time searching or looking for the validation of others to see our vision clearer.

When the only approval you need is from the person staring back at you in the mirror.

They don't believe in you?

You believe in you.

They don't support you?

You owe YOU to invest in YOU!

The more confidence you have in you,

The less you focus on,

The less you worry about what people think about you,

What they say about you,

How they feel about you or what you do.

See

You are so concerned about what other people feel about you.

You don't know how you feel about you.

At some point you have to say to yourself

It doesn't matter if you don't like me.

I like ME.

Don't force yourself to be someone else's fantasy

Because someone's opinion of you

Does not have to become your reality.

How other people feel about **you** is *none of your business!*

Quit putting so much stock in what THEY say and 'Get out yo' feelings!'

You'd go against your own belief just to be liked?

Be something they want you to be just for likes?

Doesn't matter how they feel about you,

How do *YOU* feel about *YOU*?

Love yourself,

When you love yourself

Don't try to convince others to do the same.

If you base *your* feelings about *you* off their feelings

That's just insane.

What is he gonna think?

What is she gonna think?

What will they say?

Hush!

Listen up.

Your decisions

Are *YOUR* decisions.

You care too much.

Date Her Like You Just Met Her

Part 1

I know you've been with her for a long time,

You're working hard to provide for your family and you barely have time.

When she's arguing, fighting, fussing, and complaining seemingly every day for no reason

Maybe she's really trying to tell you that she misses how you used to date her when you first met her

And did nice things frequently and not just during birthday and holiday season.

She keeps telling you people make time for what they want,

Well, show her you want her.

The same things you did to get her

You'll have to do to keep her.

If you didn't have to do these things to get her,

Do them anyway to make her a believer.

Your goal should always be to turn her inside out, make her heart speak

Kiss her slowly, whisper you love her softly in her ear, make her knees weak.

Throughout a long day, text her and get a Lil flirty.

Get dressed up, go scoop her up like you don't live together, around 7:30.

Show up with flowers, open her door, pull out her chair, make her feel special.

Make her understand that for her, there's no limit to the things you want to do.

Talk to her!

Sex –

It's much deeper than a physical penetration

Show her she's not just another body to you.

Dig deep within her mind, make love with her thoughts,

Penetrate her cerebral cortex with no hesitation.

When you get home, take your time, no need to rush.

Allow your mouth to occupy the space that's near her lips.

Gently massage the outer portion of her hips

Serenade her with compliments of how beautiful she is.

Lubricate her thoughts with words that are clever.

I'm not trying to tell you how to love your woman,

I just stopped by to say

Never get complacent

Always date her like you just met her.

Date Her Like You Just Met Her

Part 2

Let's go, back to the days when you couldn't get her off
your mind,

Every time you saw her you got butterflies

Back to the middle of the day random text for no reason

The times where you would use your fly lines to say
something cheesy and have her cheesin'

Those moments that you realized that knowing how to
touch her

Without touching her really touches her.

See, now you've gotten complacent, and the feeling is
gone

Just because the thrill of the chase is,

Because now, you feel you got her.

But some way we gotta get back to speaking life into
her,

Don't ignore her presence

Ask her about her day

See how she's really doing.

Say something that makes her blush and smile from cheek to cheek.

And when she gets home, after a long day, massage her mind, massage her back, rub her feet.

On a day when she's not feeling herself, tell her that she's beautiful.

Lean over, kiss her on her cheek, whisper in her ear all the wonderful things you want to do to her

Make her feel wanted, make her feel loved, always reassure.

Break your neck for her like you did when you were first trying to get at her

And the love will always be pure.

When her emotions are all over the place, be gentle and
kiss her face

Let her know that to be wrapped in your arms, there's
no better or safer place.

Randomly smack her on the backside when she walks
past,

Let her know she's still got it.

And that no matter how big or small she gets

Your attraction, your love will never change

And there's nothing she can do about it.

Never get too comfortable because you got her,

There's always room for improvement

We can always do better

But really all we really have to do is

Date her like you just met her.

Be His Medicine

Part 1

Let him know you still value the man the he is, and the things he does

Sometimes his self-value may not to him seem so valuable

See the strength of a woman lies not below her waist or between her thighs

But it's that look in her eyes

When she looks in his eyes, rubs his head, and lets him know everything is going to be alright

Understand that the power you possess has the ability to relieve stress

With a soft caress that's deeper than sex.

It's the ability to speak life into him when it seems he has nothing left

Just gently kiss him on his forehead and lay his head on your chest.

After a long day and he's hurting

Something's bothering him and you don't know what to say

Know that as a woman you are so powerful

You're the key to his world

Not because you're aggressive or demanding

But the strength and power lie in you being able to completely destroy him or build him up,

Only using your words.

So, choose the latter

Cut out the negative chatter,

Encourage him, support him, listen to his dreams

Believe in his vision even if you can't see what he sees

Dote on him, Love on him, Tell him he's Fine as Hell.

Be His Medicine Not His Headache

Part 2

The last thing a man wants to do

After fighting the battles of the world

Is come home to his woman and fight round 2.

His home should be his place of peace.

He shouldn't want to take the long way home.

He should be rushing home happy to see you,

But that's on you.

When he wraps his arms around you

His problems for the moment should disappear

He should feel as if he had wings and could soar.

So, don't hit him with a thousand things,

Nag him or complain to him 5 minutes after he walks through the door.

You're not just doing this for him

You're doing it for yourself.

Give him that kind of vibe you know he can't find

anywhere else.

I know you have your issues.

You have a career too.

Sometimes it doesn't hurt to cook for him

And let him know how much he means to you.

No, I'm not asking you to be perfect,

I know things get bad.

He makes you mad.

Or maybe he fell a little short on his bills this month

And that wasn't part of the plan.

It's in these moments, that what you say

Is the most important, even though he fell short,

Be mindful of what you say.

Never make him feel like less of a man

Talk **to** him

Not **at** him, as if he is *your son*.

Yeah, outwardly he appears strong

But honestly

On the inside

There are certain words

Certain situations he's sensitive to

Things that'll have him feeling insecure like he's not man enough for you.

This is where you swoop in with your cape like superwoman.

Here to save the day.

Look deeply into his eyes

Kiss him on his lips and tell him you have faith in him.

Everything is going to be ok.

Be his medicine not his headache.

Unimportant

She asks you a thousand times

how this dress looks on her

how her hair looks

do you still find her attractive

if you still really love her

to all of these you frustratingly answer yes.

not fully understanding why she continues to ask you
the same questions over and over

as if your answer will one-day change

and through your eyes she won't look the same

or somehow your love for her won't stay the same

and to you that's insane

but a woman needs constant reassurance

and I know it's irritating sometimes

but try looking at it through her eyes

or here you can have mine

our job is to constantly have her mind on cloud nine

thank her for the little things she does for us

and let her know they don't go unnoticed

flirt with her

compliment her

on her hair

her body

she'd be glad that you noticed

look past her emotions

hear past her nagging

and try to hear what she's really saying

the more you listen

notice

and elevate her

makes her that much less available for another man

yeah, you're the man

so, you want her to need you

but don't hold back

don't be afraid to let her know

that her contributions to your life

are as equally important

you need her too

watch how you speak to her

pay attention to your tone in how you say what you say

make her feel appreciated

and not like she's your child

or your maid

quit acting as if her feelings are a sponge

and thinking no matter what you do

because you pay the bills

and buy her nice things

she's gonna absorb it

you know that old saying

what you won't do

another one will

so, quit making her feel

Unimportant.

It's Ok!

Black man

I know,

I know the world can be a cold cruel place

I know it's getting harder to even put food on the plate

I know it feels like we gotta be hard, be tough 24/7

We've always been taught to show and prove our masculinity at all times

Not be so sensitive, so soft, never walk that line

You can't always be tough, but I'm here to tell you

It's ok to love.

That woman that's been by your side

Always down to ride

She's waiting on you to tell her you miss her

Your daughter

That lil' beautiful girl with the gorgeous smile

She's waiting for you to pick her up, hug her, and kiss her

Your son

No! Not your lil' homie or lil' nigger, but that young man that looks just like you,

The one that you don't even see

Tries to walk, stand, talk, and hold his hands just like you

He's waiting on you

To spend some time with him,

He's waiting on that father and son bond

Looking for your approval in everything he does

Longing for your attention

Just waiting on you to say you're proud of him.

I know you believe that tough love is the best love,

It will make him tough, and he won't go to jail like the rest of em'.

What you don't understand is...

If you're too hard on him, you get the opposite effect,

I promise

It's OK...

Show love instead.

She told you she wanted a real man that's true,

But she didn't want you to play the role of her father

She just wanted the husband in you.

If you're too tough, you run the risk of pushing her
away.

Lighten up, listen to her share her feelings

Listen to her vent, let her rant, open up, show a little
emotion

It's Ok....

That doesn't make you less of a man.

What You Look Like

James: Maybe it's just me, but I just don't get it.

You dress half naked, I make a sexual comment, and I'm thirsty and pathetic.

Tasha: I wear clothes to accentuate make my curves. I can't help I got a big butt.

Just because I dress like this, don't make me a slut.

James: You got a lot going, so I wanted to holla at you. What kind of comments did you expect when you dressed like that?

Tasha: Your approach was all wrong. All you want is to get in these drawers.

James: Well, you showing them. Got everything on display Baby.

Tasha: But, I am a woman, not a low life tramp. Don't come at me like that. I'm still a lady.

James: I'm sooo confused. You dress like that, knowing you're gonna draw attention. Got your goods all out, and I'm the one that's tripping.

Tasha: I just like to look good. I'm grown. That don't mean I sleep with everybody.

Old Woman (standing nearby): Well, let me interject something that will help everybody. How a man approaches you is all based on what you look like. Now that doesn't excuse the disrespect or make it right. What he sees when he sees you is how he perceives you. It's all about presentation. Once again, it doesn't make the disrespect right, but it does determine his approach. If you feel what I'm sayin'. No, it's not all about what you wear, but if you want a better response from men be careful of what you put out there. And once again it doesn't make it right, but a guy's approach is based off what you look like. To my fellas - Be very careful.   Not every woman you meet, who dresses like that is a dummy or a tramp.   Get it together men. Most are actually quite intelligent. So, it's cool to admire those curves and that body of hers, but don't be so aggressive, so disrespectful. Treat her with the respect a beautiful queen deserves. Be subtle, be gentle, let her know she's attractive, and that you like her. Quit being so quick to judge her based on what she looks like.

He Don't Love You

You're in love with him so your vision is blurry,

Real love doesn't leave you bloody swollen, beaten, and hurting.

You keep lying to yourself about the same things,

Maybe things will get better

You know people change.

But the more you take him back

The worse it gets.

Now he's escalating

Doing it in front of the kids.

Your love for him is crippling.

It's getting harder to leave

Harder to hide the marks on your face

It's getting easier for your daughter to see.

Do you *really* want your daughter to believe that *this* is the way love is supposed to be?

Your kids aren't stupid.

They know what's going on.

Every time they wake up

There's a new hole in the wall.

You can try to talk all day, but they pay way more attention to what you do than what you say.

Your son will grow up believing this is how a woman is to be treated.

Your daughter will believe she's supposed to let a man beat her.

Why does the pain seem to draw you closer to him?

If you don't wanna do it for yourself, then do it for them.

How many times will you take him back because he said he won't do it again?

When he tells you he won't do it again,

He does it again.

You're way too beautiful

Way too intelligent

To continue to get hurt.

You gotta find your Inner Queen baby girl and know your worth.

You're way more than his punching bag

But you don't wanna leave

You feel imprisoned, because he's your children's dad.

Close friends and family begging you to leave

Before it's too late.

Your brothers and uncles wanna get involved, but you tell them no thanks.

They just don't wanna see someone they love

So dearly

Be the victim of **another** senseless murder.

You're still tryna make sense of it all and say to yourself,

How could you beat the mother of your kids?

How could you believe that he loves you when he could care less if you lived?

Too stubborn to leave

This time he's gone off the deep end

Now you're laid up in ICU

Surrounded by family and friends

Cards, flowers, get well balloons, and...

Mama crying,

Saying,

Gone

too

soon.

We Got to Do Better

Your hair is slayed, you're looking fly, cute outfit, and nails done.

But......you're walking with a baby girl that looks like she belongs to no one.

Doesn't even look as if she belongs with ya'.

What's wrong with this picture?

Fly clothes, nice haircut, tapered fade with the line

But......when it comes to doing the same for your kids

You claim to not have the money, nor the time.

You spend money on kids that aren't yours, but to your own, you can't be a father figure.

What's wrong with this picture?

Your son got on the new J's,

But he's bringing home bad grades.

Help me, 'cause I don't get ya'.

We'd rather focus on his looks and undervalue his education.

Something's wrong with this picture.

He's at home wasting his life away playing video games.

Meanwhile to support him and your family,

You're working hard, slaving, working 12 hours a day.

Using your car, not to contribute to the house or look for a job,

But to chill with his boys and joyride.

After your shift is over he has the audacity to leave you waiting outside.

As beautiful as you are,

There must be other guys who have it together

Swarming to try to get with ya'

But you're so in love with this guy.

Something's wrong with this picture.

You pay all the bills, but he lives with you.

Something's wrong with this picture.

Driving a brand-new BMW,

But you live at home with your mom.

Looks like your priorities are out of line.

But…. you don't see the problem, you think it's fine.

Club every weekend,

But can barely pay your bills.

As if spending money you don't have will make you richer.

Something's wrong with this picture.

He's sitting in the car

Sitting on his backside while you pump gas and put air in the tires.

As a man not doing what he's supposed to do,

He gets mad if another man notices and approaches,

Asks if he can do the job, he's supposed to do and pump the gas for you.

Whatever happened to opening doors, pulling out chairs, and pay for dinner

Walking on the outside, letting her walk on the inside.

These things

Are so simple.

It's crazy how many people don't get the picture that

Something's wrong with this picture.

We GOT to do Better!

Differences

The time has long passed from the days we used to joke and laugh

From back in the day even though you had your own food you would reach on my plate

Just to eat what I had

Now things are a little different

Barely can stand to look at my face

So, at the house you destroyed all my pictures

I know we no longer love each other but why do we have to hate on each other

Why do we have to fall into that trap, tired of seeing that

I mean just because we no longer see eye to eye doesn't mean we can't still stand side by side

We got kids involved so at this point it's not about us at all

It would've been selfish to still stay together just for the kids

I'd rather them see us happy apart rather than bitter and fighting all the time, that's no way to live

Staying together even though we knew we shouldn't does more harm than good

The kids will grow up not really knowing how to properly show affection,

How to properly communicate

All because they grew up in a house where we acted as if we hated to see each other's face

Think about how it looks through their eyes and the drastic effect it would have on their lives

If all they see us do is fuss and fight

Yeah, I know that's the stereotype

But why can't we stop the cycle

We can still share laughs even though it will never be how it used to be

Our unity concerning their lives will teach them how to deal with adversity

Let them see that they don't have to choose sides

This is bigger than you and me

Even though it's not a two-parent home, the bond between the two parents is still strong

I don't have to hate you

You don't have to hate me.

Let Me Talk to 'em

(Absent Father)

Keith:

When the first memory of your mom is her crying and trying to figure out which bill to pay and her repeatedly saying to herself, "God's gonna make a way. God's gonna make a way."

I often sit back and ask what made it this way. Gave you excuses for not being there. Put it all on mom and said maybe she ran you away.

She would go nights barely eating so I wouldn't starve. Then go crying with her head in the pillow, so I wouldn't see her scars.

So, I tried to play ball hoping that my talent would impress you.

That didn't work, so I ran the streets, homie, just to get next to you.

Your street rep preceded itself, so I'm just hoping that when you look at me you can see yourself

Maybe that'll make you love me more and spend more time with me now that I'm just like you,

I got my pants sagging and I'm rolling up the swishers.

In and out of jail, just to catch your attention.

To my surprise, that **still** didn't work, and no one could prepare me for the hurt.

Searching for your love, coming up empty, every time.

Say?   What do I have to do to get love from this daddy of mine.

So, I give up on it, becoming another statistical hood kid, "good" turned more to the streets 'cause it felt big homie nem gave me more love than you did.

All I ever wanted was your love and your time man. Money didn't matter and all because of lack of your love I'm laying on this cold concrete bleeding to death with

my mom holding a sign and wearing a t shirt talking
about BLACK LIVES MATTER

Jasmine:

There's nothing worse than a man who can be
everything to everybody except a father to his own
child.

I was never daddy's little girl or daddy's little princess. I
grew up always insecure about myself, so when a guy
shows me a little attention, I mistake his intentions.

Not sure of how to feel about myself, I mean, *you* don't
love me, which makes *me* not love me, so how can I
ever really expect them to. The moment anyone shows
a lil' interest that's what I cling to.

How can I ever understand the love of a man, and what
he is or isn't supposed to do? When the first man that
was ever supposed to love me, broke my heart before
another man had the chance to.

Now, people judge my relationship choices and say that I'm ignorant. But, where were they? More importantly where were you when all those cousins, uncles, and friends of the family were taking away my innocence and there was no one I could tell. I just had to suck it up and live with it.

You moved on with your life. Meanwhile, I'm living through physical and verbal abuse.

Imagine the hurt I felt to know you lived around the corner the whole time, being the perfect father, raising someone else's kids, that don't even look like you.

A Different Point of View

Some say the reason for not even seeing the kids is 'cause she's bitter

And she's making it harder.

Some say child support is snatching all my funds barely leaving me something to eat

So why even bother.

So, I slave and put in long hours at a job with good benefits and great pay

But I barely got enough money left to feed my face or a place to stay.

Yeah you can say you did the crime so you gotta do the time

But how can I truly take care for a child of mine when I can barely survive.

I can understand the guys who don't give a damn about their kids.

What about the father who's just trying to make sure his kid's life is more blessed than his?

What about the man that's trying to be there every step of the way?

He's losing more of his heart with every garnishment of his pay.

Soo.... Is it that a man loses love or interest in his kids? Becoming more regretful of his life's decisions, more bitter.

Or is that the man who once wanted to be a good father is discouraged by the system making the vision of seeing *his* kids less visible.

Now.... they see less of 'em and the cycle continues.

When a man can't pay for his child, he goes to jail.

When women can't pay, she receives welfare.

How is that fair?

That's no excuse for him nor any disrespect to the women, the single mothers out here who are struggling every day to make a way

But more of an eye opener for what might've made him that way.

Seemingly so cold

So heartless

And it's hard for him to take.

Man, you gotta be a father regardless.

So, the weaker man leaves and uses the harsh realities as a way out.

Salute to the fathers still pursuing a relationship with their kids

While he's still trying to find a way out.

He understands the impact he could have on his child's life

Regardless of his feelings toward the mother or ex-wife.

In a society where it's not hard to see

The Man's Manhood getting torn, beat down, and destroyed continuously.

You got books, every talk show host, every social media icon, and the system

Catering to and geared toward the women

Specifically

Tremendously.

Sooo, I shared this word to offer

No excuse,

Because, a father should be a father despite what he's going through

And the kids never asked to be here.

Of course, you gotta pay your dues.

I just simply stopped by to

Offer you a different point of view.

She's Watching You!

Everything you do from the way you comb your hair to those stylish clothes you wear

To the way you care for and treat yourself

She's watching you.

She is paying attention to what you say and what you do

How you respond to pressure situations - adversity and negativity.

So, always display to her the woman that you would want her to grow up to be.

You're her mom first

Before you begin to twerk, never lose sight of *your* worth.

Before you trade in your motherhood for "likes"

Remember every decision you make effects another life.

No, it's not a good idea for her to meet every guy you date

Or have men coming in and out of her life.

Before you do what you do

Always remember

She's watching you!

Friend of the Family

How could you not see it? How could you turn a blind eye to it?

I mean, all the signs were there

You just chose to ignore them.

I even tried to tell you, but you threatened me and told me to close my mouth.

Say nothing to no one 'cause what happens in this house stays in this house.

You **had** to notice the look in his eyes when he saw me, how he cut his eyes as I walked by.

The way he walked up on me from behind when I would be in the kitchen washing dishes.

Your only response would be, "Quit being so mean! He just playing with you."

Your love for him caused you to seemingly forget about me. Didn't it?

How could you be so deeply in love with him after he's done all these things to me?

Violating me. No peace at home and with him, you *still* left me alone.

How could you relinquish to him so much power?

The bathroom was my only escape until he started bursting in on me in the shower.

Knife ready to go.

My only escape was my imagination. Picturing, wishing, and praying that my current situation was not my final destination.

Though only lasting briefly, because like a ton of bricks, my reality would rush back and hit me.

For most kids, it was just a folktale, but to me the boogeyman seemed so real.

I *finally* got the courage to tell other family, but 'everything's gonna be alright' seemed to be their only advice.

No matter how hard I cried or who I told nothing seemed to make it right.

All people ever said was, 'Girl, he wouldn't do that. He's a friend of the family.'

No one would believe that this guy, you call a friend of the family, would be molesting me.

Sometimes, I barely got any sleep at night.

So, I started going to bed while tightly gripping a knife

Constantly repeating to myself, 'This ends tonight, this ends tonight, this ends tonight'.

When he pulled the covers back, all my frustrations began to flow and took control.

Now, I'm writing you this letter from the pen, doing 25 to life.

Even after allll of the evidence, nobody could believe or wrap their minds around the fact that I could ever be hurt by such a

Close **friend** of the family.

From the Start

(To a Mother from a Son)

Born into this world with two strikes, we're black and we're men.

It's guaranteed we''ll have a tougher path.

You, as the mother, are the main influence.... so why add to it – strike 3.

With no father figure present, it's hard to find someone who'll identify with my presence.

So, we grow up aimlessly with a scarcity of men who look like me.

The only thing you seem to see when you look at me

Is the guy who left you 7 months into your pregnancy.

Because he left in a quick flash, I get all the backlash.

When you tell me - I'll never be nothing - I'm gonna be just like my daddy,

It immediately lowers my self-esteem.

This constant verbal abuse is driving me insane,

But, what's even worse is it's sinking into my brain

Killing my dreams, destroying my visions before I could even get started.

I'm not your muthaf..., your bi..., your h..,

I'm not stupid, I'm not retarded.

Are you so blind to see, so selfish to believe

Your words won't matter to me?

Your words are powerful, and they hurt.

They're like cancer, killing me slowly.

Making me have thoughts like - since I'm not gonna be nothing anyway,

I might as well start robbing folks with Lil' Tony,

I'll always dream of the moment when someone would stand up for me and tell you to

Watch how you talk to me.

This is no way to live.

How could I ever believe in me, if all I know and have heard inside my house is what seems to be a bitter black woman cursing at her kids.

Being successful to me is but an imaginative thought, I was never taught.

Taught what it is to be a real man or dream as far as the stars

Because in my heart

Your words are battle scars.

Which is why....

I'm in this prison cell writing you this letter

From the heart

Telling you, how you, whether you wanted to believe it or not,

Damaged me

From the start.

Help Me Understand (Confused Brother)

It seems like everywhere we turn, black male bashing
has become a trending fashion.

Seems to be the trending topic when everyone wants to
cash in.

It's like everyone takes a turn, takes a poke,

Everyone is in on the joke.

Every radio, social media personality, and talk show
host,

I understand, make a product to cater toward the
women,

Give them what they want to hear, and you'll make your
money,

That's your ploy.

And if a couple of brothers get hurt along the way,

So be it.

It's just a casualty of war.

Now, I get it, a lot of us have our problems, and there may be more than a few.

How can you so boldly, heartlessly, help tear down men in a race,

That look just like you?

Take into consideration most of us weren't and haven't been taught what it really *is* to be a Man.

So instead of bashing and talking down on us, help us understand.

Teach us the do's and don'ts of what it is to be a man.

Let me help you understand before you open your mouth again.

Have you ever stopped to think that we gain nothing from the bashing?

Instead of lessons and guidance

We're left feeling belittled and embarrassed.

Who is that helping?

We've heard it our entire lives in many different forms and aren't bettered by it.

In fact, I'm convinced that some are so beat down by it,

They say to themselves, 'Why even try.'

My message is not meant to exclude or excuse the behavior.

Wrong is wrong at the end of the day,

I'm just simply asking

Instead of talking about us

Show us the way.

Sincerely,

A Confused Brother

Black Dollar

When I read headlines and tag lines that state:

With a current buying power of $1 Trillion, they spend two times the amount they make. The importance of connecting with African-American consumers is more important than ever.

It makes me wonder why aren't we more clever

They made us love their wealth and hate ourselves.

They then create and design products geared toward the black community

To make us contribute to their wealth and pass up businesses run by people that look like you and me.

When will we get it?

That, if we supported our own like we support them, we'd all make millions.

The black dollar is a powerful dollar.

Don't be fooled.

The only problem is we don't shop with and don't spend it with

Or support people that look just like us.

Oh, you don't believe it's powerful

Just ask Crystal and Tommy Hilfiger or any other established company

That decides to use the word nigger.

Look at the dramatic difference of the "before" and "after" percentage

Of when we supported and shopped with them and when we didn't.

It's no secret they study us. Research our likes and our shopping and buying habits.

Pay attention to internet, tv, and radio advertising

They all seem to focus specifically on black audiences and the black demographic.

What will it take to get through to you?

We set trends and make movements with everything we do.

Everyone wants to be a part of the black business and get a piece of the black pie.

Except for blacks, right?

See, our need to belong and be accepted by other races, has plagued us

To where we rarely want to support business of people with the same faces.

Imagine if we supported each other like we supported them.

Imagine what the community would look like then.

More millionaires, more entrepreneurs

Less black on black crime, more scholars

All because we understood the power of

The **Black Dollar.**

Real Life

This section is composed of stories from my uncle, who was a successful businessman at one point in his life. Unfortunate things happened in his life, which caused him to lose all faith and hope in himself and completely let himself go. We all have that person we know that becomes a comedian and a philosopher every time they get drunk, well that person is my uncle, and these are his stories.

One Day

Sitting at the stop light, I look over to my right and I see my uncle flagging me down. I roll down the window and he yells:

Unc: Nepheeewww!!!

Me: Wassup Unc?

Unc: Pull over let me politic with you for a second. I'm about drop some more knowledge on you before the light turns green. So, I pull over into the parking lot.

Me: Go 'head. I'm listening fam.

Unc: (takes two sips of his blue top) Use this on your channel...... Quit being a vitamin all your life a one a day.

He laughs and walks completely off! Didn't look back. No explanation or nothing. Once again, this dude said somethin' to make me think, and as I'm driving it hits me.:

Don't be a "*one day*" type of person. You know, "One day I'm going to have this, be that, or do that." That "*one day*" will never come if you don't take the steps on

"*This Day*" to have what you want or get to where you want to be. Every journey, every dream begins with one step, but you gotta take the first step. Yesterday, you said, "*Tomorrow*." There are a lot of people who yesterday said, "*Tomorrow*," and didn't make it to see today. Quit procrastinating. The time is always NOW. The attitude should always be, **Now or Never**!

No Sleep

Some people you just never expect to learn anything from. One afternoon my uncle walked over to me and said:

Unc: I see you do a lot of motivational stuff but, let me drop this knowledge. Let me drop this science on you fam.

Me: Say what's on your mind.

(Unc takes two sips of his blue top and says...)

Unc: You can't go to sleep, if you don't close your eyes.

Me: (crying laughing) Huh? Wait, what!?

Unc: Yeah, yeah. I knew that was too deep for you. All I'm saying is grind now, sleep later. You gotta sacrifice some sleep to be great. You must sacrifice. If you don't sacrifice for what you want, then what you want becomes the sacrifice!

Me:(Scratching my head, mouth wide open, laughing,

and thinking to myself)

Did that just come from him?

Don't Settle for Safe

It's the middle of the night. I hear a knock
at the door, and it's my uncle. This guy wanted to know
if I had some Kool-Aid, because the store was closed.

Me: Wait...wait... Man it's 2 o'clock in the morning. What
do want with Kool-Aid?

Unc: Well that's kinda slow.   Obviously, I want
to drink it.

I let him in.

Me: Man, I'm not even going to
entertain you right now. Kool-Aid is in the drawer.

He makes the Kool-Aid, pours it in a cup,
and then pulls a liquor bottle out of his pocket.
He takes a sip.

Unc: Yeah see.   That's all that was missing.

He walked over to the table where I was, looked at my

business plans, or what was left of them. I had balled

them up.

Unc: What's wrong with you?

Me: It's way too risky to pull these things off. I got bills, I got these kids. I would be sacrificing a lot.   My safest bet would probably be to stay where I am.

He laughed and said:

Unc: For you to be so smart, you stupid.

Me: (Angrily) You think it's funny.?!?

Unc: (Yelling) YEP!

   Then Unc laughed again, took another sip, and put his hands on my shoulder.

Unc: An Airplane is always safer on the ground, but that ain't what it was meant for.

   He laughed again at himself and said, "Yeah, yeah, that was a good one right there. I surprised myself with that one. Then he yelled thanks for the Kool-Aid and walked out.

   I was stuck and stunned, because yet again he was right. You see, in life, we must quit settling for safe. Quit focusing on comfort. Everything that we ever wanted in life is right on the other side of our comfort zone. In order to be successful, you must take risks, you have to jump. Of course, it's much safer and easier staying content where you are, but if you ever get tired of mediocrity, living paycheck to paycheck, not having things when you want or need them most, if you ever truly wanna be successful you must take a chance on yourself. You owe you to find out what you truly can do and who you truly can be. If you keep settling for safe, you'll never know. A plane is much safer on the ground, but that ain't what it was meant for.

Two Sides to Pain

I come home after the greatest basketball game of my life. We won the championship, and I was the reason! There is also some disappointment and frustration in my eyes.

My uncle says:

Unc: Boy, what's wrong with you? You got a splinter in your butt cheeks from sitting on the bench too long? 'Cause I know they didn't let your sorry butt in the game.

Seeing that I wasn't laughing or talking trash like I usually would, he crept over.

Unc: Boy, you crying? You kids these days are so sensitive. Go change your panties and let me know when you're ready to talk about it.

When he said that, I could no longer hold my laughter. It was entirely too funny, especially his facial expression.

Unc: What's wrong?

Me: I'm tired of seeing everybody's families always being there at the games supporting them. Mom and

Dad cheering them on, but when I look around no one is ever there for me. How come I couldn't have a dad and mom who were there for me like the other kids?

Unc: Sit down. Let me tell you a story. There once were twin brothers, you could barely tell them apart. Their mother was on drugs and all through their life their father was in and out of prison. He was on and off drugs and always into trouble. One of the twins allowed the pain, of not having a father and not knowing his mother, make him become very negative, very nonchalant about life. He displayed actions of not truly caring about himself or anyone else. He let that pain drive him into dark places of depression and aggression. He began to hang with thugs and soon became the leader of his crew. Multiple women got pregnant by him, and then he had kids that he didn't care for. His response anytime anyone would ask him why he wasn't in his kids' life he would say, "I ain't have my father here with me. Nobody taught me how to be a man, so why do I need to teach them. Those kids will be alright." Soon after a fight at a night club, he was shot and killed by a rival gang.

His brother, the other twin, chose a different route. By this time, he also had kids, but the way he thought was totally different from his brother. He felt the fact that he didn't have his father in his life helped him understand the pain of not being there for your children. He took pride in being a father. Not having his father, made him go harder. He finished college, got several degrees, built several businesses, and became very successful.

Unc: The moral of the story is that at some point we're all gonna go through something. At some point, life is gonna hit us hard until it hurts. It's at this point that you feel the pain that you have is a defining choice to make. Either you let the pain use you or you use the pain. Use the pain to push harder, do not give up on your dreams, your goals, and what you want out of life. Are you going to quit the first-time life hits you in the mouth and you feel a little discomfort? Are you gonna tell pain "I know you're coming, I'm ready, and there's nothing you can do to stop me?" Will you say, "Ok pain. You've repeatedly hit me in my mouth. I only have one tooth left, but I'm ready to lose that one too if I must."

Being Happy is a Choice

I woke up one Friday morning tired, frustrated, and thinking about all the things I hadn't accomplished the previous day. I was thinking about all the things that would transfer over to my to do list for today, on top of everything I must do today. Out walks my uncle happy and cheerful as can be. Loudly and forcefully saying, "Good Morning!!" Unc went straight to the fridge, drank his beer as if it were a protein shake or energy drink saying, "Yes, yes, always need one of these to get my day started." Then he laughed at himself like he always does, looked at me, and said, "I said good morning. I didn't sleep with you last night."

Me: I heard you.

Unc: When somebody speaks you're supposed to speak back, so Good Morning.

Me: What's so good about it?

He laughed and said.......

Unc: IF YOU DON'T BELIEVE IT'S A GOOD MORNING, YOU JUST TRY MISSING ONE.

Afterwards I laughed loudly and said:

Me: You couldn't be more right.

Your day will go exactly how the corners of your mouth turn in the morning. Being happy is a choice, so choose to be happy. Choose to be optimistic in the midst of any problem. Always find the positive in a negative situation. Always be grateful for what you do have instead focusing on what you don't have. God woke you up this morning. There are a lot of people who can't say the same. So, smile through it all.

Anyway

In the midst of one of my toughest moments in life, I have financial trouble and the lights are off.
At the same time two of my friends are sending me pictures. One is closing the deal on his dream home and the other just rode off the lot in his dream car.
I'm holding my phone and saying to myself,
"Dang man! Why are they coming up like this and I'm over here struggling?" At this point I find myself pissed at their success.

Meanwhile, my uncle brings four candles in the living room where I'm sitting and puts them on the table in front of me.

Unc: Nephew!!! Let me put a stain on your brain.

As he began to light the candles he said...

Unc: See, I can use this one candle and give light to all four candles equally and still be fully lit without reducing or diminishing its own light.

Me: Unc, what are you trying to say?

Unc: Don't be threatened by the success of others. SOMEONE ELSE'S SUCCESS doesn't dim yours, diminish yours, or stop yours from happening. Their success doesn't cancel out or void your own success. It's just their time. So, share your light, be grateful for what you have. Be genuinely happy for others. Support them, encourage them regardless of what you are going through and you will get where you are going in due time. Your time is coming. Don't be that person, so petty, so concerned with other's success that you focus only on if the ice in their drink is cooler than the ice in your drink. Focus on your own success, not the success of others.

Rearview

We were sitting on the couch watching Michael Jackson tributes and out of nowhere my uncle came from behind the couch, took a shot of his liquor, and started imitating Michael. He started doing his spins, kicking his leg, moon walking, and beating on his chest.

Tired after a couple of minutes, he flopped on the couch out of breath, laughed and said:

Unc: You know, some people live their whole life like that.

Me: What do you mean?

Unc: Doing the "Moonwalk". Some people spend their whole lives in reverse, thinking of what was, wishing they could go back and change things that were; holding on to what was. It's just like driving. There is a reason why the windshield is bigger than the rear-view mirror.

He jokingly told me...

Unc: Here's some homework. I won't be there when you try but...attempt to drive your car forward while looking in the rear-view mirror.

Me: You know that's not possible. You will miss the present and surely miss the future.

Unc: Same thing with life. If you keep looking back, you'll miss the blessings that are right in front of you and the opportunities of the future. Learn to use the past as a guide to make you better, but not to harbor any hurt, anger, resentment, or disappointment.

Let it go!!

Twerk

Sitting on the couch bored, one day while scrolling through Facebook we run across at least 10 twerking videos back to back.

Unc: Oooooowee! Look at that!

An hour later he's just sitting on the couch and out of nowhere says:

Unc: Man, that was amazing, that was something else.

Still thinking he's talking about the videos I say:

Me: Yeah, yeah. That was real nice!

Unc: Boy! I'm not talking about the booty. I'm talking about what happens in response to seeing the booty and the hours later after you've seen the booty.

With a crazy look on my face I laugh and say:

Me: What are you talking about now? I know good and well you are not about to turn twerking into another one of your motivational stories.

Unc: Just think about it. You watched the video. It got you mentally and physically stimulated just from envisioning the girls in reality. How did that happen? People don't realize how real, how powerful the power of visualization can be. We use it every day, don't truly believe in it, or know that we're using it. How is it that we can create a mental picture in our heads from what we see, and something happens to us physically? All just from seeing it in our minds. This is proof that what they say is true. If the mind can conceive it, the heart can believe it, then you can achieve it. If you are

courageous enough to think it, bold enough to speak it, then you can hold it in your hand. The same way you think those thoughts and get aroused physically. Your thoughts are real and physical. Your imagination

is God's gift to you. It is the preview for all you wish to be. You must have an unreal imagination, and you must be able to see yourself where you want to be before you get there.

Live

I'm just getting in town when I get word that one of my best friends from childhood was shot and has passed. I hop into the car with my uncle, and he takes me to the wake to view the body. Noone is in the room but Unc and myself. All I can do is stare at the casket in silence. Saying to myself, "You really don't know when your time is coming. Age doesn't matter."

My uncle walks over, pulls out a bottle from his jacket and whispers...

Unc: Hey! We can drink in here, right?

Me: Really?

He laughs and says...

Unc: Man relax. I'm just...I'm just... I'm serious.

As he sits down next to me he takes several sips then says:

Unc: One thing about life is YOU CAN'T MAKE IT OUT OF HERE ALIVE!

Then he laughs loudly.

Me: That's so insensitive to say over a dead body.

Unc: No, no, no. You not hearing me. Nobody knows when their time is going to be up. So, we got to stop being scared and procrastinating when it comes to our dreams and the things we want to do in life. You can't get out of here alive, so why not risk life when it's going to keep going. Give everything you got to your dreams and the life you want to live! You get up every day and invest your time on someone else's dream for 4, 8, 12, even 16 hours a day. You're working inside their dream, yet you don't have the guts to step out and invest that time in your own dreams. You either go after your dream or someone will hire you to work on theirs!

Distracted

After an interview, that went extremely well, I was super excited. They offered me the job along with the salary that I wanted. I came in and told my uncle. I was pumped while telling him. I said, "Unc! Listen to this. That job I've been waiting for...I got it!! Good money and good benefits!" He looked at me awkwardly and said,

Unc: Don't you ever forget this. YOUR SALARY IS THE BRIBE THEY PAY YOU TO FORGET YOUR DREAMS. Remember they are not paying you to work, they are paying you to not work for yourself.

Don't get distracted.

Wantrepreneur

It's New Year's and everybody is vibing, having drinks of their choice. Of course, *every* drink was my uncle's choice. At this point in the night, everyone is pretty much going around the room sharing their dreams and the things that they "want" to do or accomplish for the new year.

My uncle pulls me to the side and says...

Unc: It's a lot of **Wantrepreneurs** in this room. Don't you be one of em'.

Me: Wantrepreneur?

Unc: Yeah. There are three types of people in this world. Those that wish, hope, and want things to happen. Then there are those that sit back and watch things happen, and see other people fulfill their dreams/ideas that they had but were too scared to go after. Finally, there are those that make things happen with no excuses. Those are the entrepreneurs. That's who you need to be. Not a *"Want*-trepreneur"

Pain Ain't Permanent

Unc: Nephew always remember pain ain't permanent.

Me: Yes sir.

Unc: Yep, even when you're so broke you find yourself digging for coins in your ash tray.   Even when you must make that decision to miss a meal or pay a bill.   Yep, even at that point where you're down to your last, and always embarrassingly seeming to be running out of gas. You know you need it, but you're too prideful and embarrassed to ask. That moment when you walk up to the cashier and you try to whisper, "Can I get 2 dollars on number 9." Remember Nephew, pain ain't permanent.   You'll get it all in due time.

It Doesn't Matter What They See.

It's About What You See.

One rainy day my uncle gets into a wreck. The other driver was drunk and fell asleep at the wheel. After he woke up, he snatched the wheel, spun out control, and hit Unc's vehicle. The next day, the assessors came to the house and diagnosed the car as totaled. According to the insurance claim, my uncle had to get two more quotes from different auto body specialists. They all said the same thing TOTALED! The first time I looked at the vehicle I made jokes. I thought it was totaled as well. I said, "Yeah, Unc. That's nasty right there!" He looked up and laughed and said, "You can't see what I see." That same day we went to the junk yard, bought a fender, hood, door, and headlights for less than $200. We went back to the house replaced the damaged parts with the new parts, primed it to be painted, then sent it to his friend so he could paint it. That was $500. The very next week his friend pulls up in the car, and it looks better than it did before. Meanwhile my uncle is checking the mail and finds a check in the mail for his car, $6000. At this point, I'm blown away because it only took $700 to fix it, and that's when he says...

Unc: It doesn't matter what they say. All that matters is, what you see, your vision is. Your vision... you can't expect for someone else to see your vision. Everyone saw the outer appearance, but I looked at the frame that the car was built on. I looked at what it was made of. Although the outside looked defeated, I was able to restore the damaged pieces because what it was made of wasn't damaged. You guys saw one thing, I saw another.

He went on to say...

Unc: That's the same way with life. Don't trust anybody's opinion on the vision God gave you. Always go with your heart! Always trust **your** gut!

Bubble Guts

After eating a lot of Mexican food, we head home. In the middle of the drive my uncle's stomach starts bubbling and going crazy.

Unc: Woooo!! Nephew, you're going to have to speed this thing up now. My stomach won't let me wait.

Laughing, I drove a little slower just to mess with him. By the time we pulled into the driveway, he was sweating as if he had just run a marathon. When he comes out of the bathroom he says...

Unc: Your dream is just like that.

Me: Like what?

Unc: Like having the bubble guts.

Me: (Laughing) You can't be serious.

Unc: Stay with me now, I'm about to bring this one home. You can have a dream bubbling up inside of you that just *has* to come out. The more you try to suppress it and hold it in, the more it hurts. You can't stop thinking about it. You can't stop talking about it. It's always present in your mind. You may be able to stall it a little while, but soon after it comes back worse than before. If you don't let it out, it could hurt you in more ways than it would help. So, you must relax. You have to let it go. Let it flow and go for it. When you finally do that, you experience true relief.

Traffic Jam

Stuck in 5 o'clock traffic for the moment, my uncle looks over and says to me...

Unc: Following your dreams is a lot like a traffic jam. It seems like everybody is in your lane. It feels like you're not where you're supposed to be at the time you want to get there. Seems like you will never reach that break through. Remember, you must be patient, embrace the process. No need for a plan B, because it distracts you from plan A. There will always be ways that seem faster and feel like shorter routes but taking those short cuts could actually set you back further. You don't know what the traffic is like on those other streets, so stick to your guns. Stick to your dreams. Don't stray from your path no matter how frustrating the wait may be. That breakthrough is coming. Just wait for it.

No Love

Me: Yo, Unc! Why is it that when you're trying to accomplish something or get somewhere in life, it's hard for your *own* family and friends to support you?

Unc: Sometimes no support is all the support you need.

Me: I mean, yeah... ok. But... if you're not going to support, at least don't hate on my progress or talk about me behind my back. These are the people that I thought would have my back through anything.

Unc: Sometimes strangers will support you more than the people you know, 'cause the people you know have a hard time accepting that y'all came from the same place and they're still in the same place. Everybody's going to be cool with you as long as you're on the same level as they are. The moment you attempt to fulfill your potential, that admiration turns into hate. Don't get it twisted. It's not that they don't like what you're doing. It's just the fact they don't like that it's *YOU* that's doing it. Use every brick that they throw at you to build your foundation. Be prepared. They'll smile in your face and talk behind your back. Remember Nephew, Jesus wasn't betrayed by his enemies. He was betrayed by someone he considered family or a close friend, someone who was with him every day.... with a kiss at *that*.

Real Talk

DISCLAIMER: This section contains most of my favorite quotes and statements that I apply to my life. All quotes in this section are not my Own, they are quotes that I have heard or either read over the years. Most of which I couldn't determine who the originator of the quote is. However, I pray that they add value to your life as they did to mine.

Your **FEAR** of looking stupid is holding you back.

It's ok to miss the **FUN** to stack the **FUNDS**.

Life is all about perspective.

You see Impossible

I see

"**I'm** possible".

Hustle until your haters ask if you're hiring.

Hustle until you no longer
have to introduce yourself.

Giving up on your dream because of one set back

is like slashing your other three tires,

because you got one flat.

You **can't** deposit excuses.

The bank doesn't accept those.

Priorities.

They say, "I never see you at the club."

I say, "I never see you at the bank."

Don't be afraid to tell people:

"I'm going to get where I'm going.

Even if that means dropping you off."

Remember that guy that quit?

Neither does anybody else.

Let them hate.

Just be sure they spell your name right.

Show up in every single moment

Like you deserve to be there.

I used to care about what people thought

about me.

Then one day, I tried to pay my bills with

their opinions.

Don't let people put their insecurities on you.
Just because they failed at what

they were trying to do,

doesn't mean it won't work for you.

If you don't like something,

then just take away its only power ......

Your **ATTENTION.**

The only time success comes before **work**

is in the dictionary.

You're the best "**YOU**" there will ever be.

You're a terrible *"somebody else"*.

Be careful who you let speak into your life.

Understand that they can't see what you see.

A lot of people are blessed with sight

but have no vision.

Your vision is **YOUR VISION.**

Stop asking people for directions

who have never been where you are trying to go.

You can't get fired,

if you OWN the Company.

I don't accept what you expect.

I reject your negativity.

Who are you to tell me I can't have what I want

or accomplish what I want?

You may be taller than me, prettier than I am,
more muscular, or have a better shape than I have.
You may even have more money than me,

but your height, your face, your smile, your body,
your money has nothing to do with my work ethic.
You will not out work me.

Your beauty has nothing to do with my Creativity.

You will **not** out work me.

I believe in myself.

So stupid, so strong, so powerful that nothing that
you say can deter me from my goal or

tear me away from my passion.

Would you believe me?

What if I told you that there is not much of difference between you your favorite actor, athlete, comedian, or singer or whoever it is that you look up to.

At the start of each day we each are given 24 hours. The only thing that separates you from them is what they decide to do with their 24 hours.

They have the guts and the fortitude to go for what they want and the work ethic to achieve it.

Would you believe me?

Your only competition is between **YOU and YOU,** get out of your own way.

Whoever counted you out,

Obviously can't count.

If "Having bills" is the excuse

for not going after your dreams,

Wait until you get the bill for not even attempting.

They are not haters,

They're **SECRET LOVERS**.

They just can't fully *express* themselves.

You remind them of who they are not,

but who they wish to be.

The problem isn't working a 9 to 5.

The problem is the crime of you believing you don't have to work on **YOU** after 9 to 5,

On **your** dreams, on **your** business your goals.

Don't give up.

Life can go from 0 to 100 *real* quick.

If you can't build with them, don't chill with them.

Made in the USA
Columbia, SC
25 June 2018